EVERY SINGLE DAY, tens of thousands of people are hurting, suffering—**DYING** even—because of *indoor* polluted air. The *EPA* calls indoor air pollution *"America's most serious environmental problem affecting the health of humans."*

More than **50 MILLION Americans** suffer from allergies, many *caused* or *aggravated* by polluted air. Colds, sinus problems, coughing, headaches, and having to use *breathing machines* is NOT normal. Most cases CAN be prevented.

And, what about unsafe WATER? It is *everywhere*, and you need to learn the truth—the **FACTS**—from experts in their field about chlorine and fluoride and how this unsafe water affects you.

Once you understand how to *avoid* the damage this bad air and water causes, you'll live more comfortably. There is no need to hurt, or to live in pain, because of dangers you can't SEE.

This book gives you facts and answers on HOW to rid your home of these dangers quickly, safely, inexpensively, and FOREVER!

D1503066

THE SILENT KILLERS

INDOOR AIR POLLUTION

and

UNSAFE WATER

(1.5 MILLION IN PRINT)

PETE BILLAC

SWAN PUBLISHING

Author: Pete Billac
Editors: John Carlton Small; A.J. Krause; Jane Gillen
Cover Design: John Gilmore
Layout Design: Sharon Davis

OTHER BOOKS BY PETE BILLAC

The Annihilator
How Not to Be Lonely
How Not to Be Lonely—TONIGHT
The Last Medal of Honor
All About Cruises
New Father's Baby Guide
Willie the Wisp
Managing Stress
Justice is Green
The New Millionaires
Neways to a Better Life
Getting Rich on the Internet

PRINTINGS: December 1999; February 2000; March 2000 *(Revised);*
June 2000; September 2000; January 2001; March 2001; May
2001(R*evised)*; September 2001, *(Revised)* February 2002, *(Revised.*
Title change to THE SILENT KILLERS September 2002 to include
information on water. October 2002. November 2002 *(up-dated).*

Copyright @ September 2002 Swan Publishing
Library of Congress Catalog Card #2002110016
ISBN# 0-943629-52-7

The Silent Killers, is available in quantity discounts through SWAN
Publishing, 1059 CR 100, Burnet, TX 78611. Call at: (512) 756-6800,
Fax (512) 756-0102 or e-mail: swanbooks@ghg.net
Printed in the United States of America.

INTRODUCTION

This is a VERY LONG introduction. I feel I need this space to establish some *rapport* with you and to explain my writing *style*. Reading "technical stuff" can be boring.

As a nontechnical human being, I am totally unfamiliar with the *science* behind much of what I research. Once I understand what these doctors and scientists are "saying" I put an explanation in "ordinary" words for everyone to understand.

"Pure" writers, grammarians and English teachers *chide* me on my writing. They tell me about *dangling participles, sentence structure, tense* and *gerund phrases* (like I care). I'm not certain I know what those are. My main goal in writing is COMMUNICATION and SUBSTANCE.

Few of my critics have ever written a best seller: I've written 46. No bragging. I am THRILLED. Every time one of my books sells a couple of hundred thousand copies I pass a mirror, look in and almost *spit* on myself I'm so thankful.

I must have done *some* good things in the past because God has smiled on me. I'm healthy, making money, I'm helping others and I enjoy life. Many others are not, due to some illness they can't explain. I'LL try to explain them.

Every day you hear more and more horror stories about how others have been affected by air that is stale, polluted or about those who live in a house with mold and mildew. How many of you know the TRUE dangers of indoor polluted air?

I didn't even give it a thought until it happened to me. We're all human, and *rarely* does ANYONE care about anything until it happens to *them* or to those they love. When my small son became a victim, I began looking for answers.

I, like many of you, had never even "heard" about the effect *INDOOR* polluted air can have on our bodies. If I did hear about it, I ignored it. Enough problems are going on each day in the world that I can't take the time to concern myself over some new danger "made up" by somebody who wants to make money by scaring people.

Besides *"This could never be a problem with me,"* I told myself. *"My house is clean, the entire family bathes every day, we have filters on our air conditioners, we all take vitamins, I'M SAFE."*

But, then, It DID happen to me! At age two my little boy became ill. Every two months for five to nine days for more than **four years** I watched him lying there with migraine headaches, high fever and he was in pain. I shared that pain. Parents know what I mean. It's almost like watching your child drown and be unable to save them.

We spent hundreds of thousands of dollars flying him to specialists around the world to find a cure and NONE had an answer. We tried pills, they conducted countless tests, fed him certain foods and experimented with dozens of various types of medications.

I "stumbled" onto an answer one evening while giving a talk on a new book I had written titled NEW FATHER'S BABY GUIDE. Once I found a cure for my son, I began my research and then wrote this book to tell others how to prevent this from happening to them or to their loved ones.

I read books and searched the Internet. I listened to tapes, gathered pamphlets, looked for programs on TV and met with engineers, scientists and environmentalists. I *dug* for answers. Some of the FRIGHTENING statistics I uncovered were listed by governmental agencies and research groups who study these problems.

According to the *Department of Consumer Affairs*, **CHILDREN** and **THE ELDERLY** are the ones *especially* who are adversely affected by polluted indoor air. The immune system on the kids is not strong enough to fight off these contaminants and with the older people, age has made their immune systems weaker.

Not only that, everyone in the *middle group* is harmed also; these indoor air pollutants are CUMULATIVE. No matter how strong or healthy you are, they are adding up as you breathe in your own home or office and they do it *without warning*.

The American College of Allergists say that 50% (HALF) of all illnesses are caused by polluted indoor air. They say that 10 to 12 MILLION Americans suffer from asthma and that asthma is the SINGLE LARGEST CAUSE of hospital visits by children!

Yet *another* frightening statistic, according to the *World Health Organization*, is that 40 percent of all **BUILDINGS** pose a "serious health hazard" due to *indoor* air pollution. And, *Legionnaire's Disease* continues to claim lives.

In this (10th) rewrite of this book, I changed the title to killer**S**. I included WATER because it is also a major problem. Air and water are essential to life, and CLEAN air and CLEAN water are essential to a *healthy* life.

I am NOT an alarmist. I don't have a *Micro-wave Oven Diffuser* or an *Alien Shield* over my house. I have no burglar bars on my windows nor do I own a burglar alarm. I do, however, know that impure air and unsafe water will hurt us.

In going through this book, know that what I've written are FACTS compiled from billions of dollars of scientific research and hundreds of years of combined studies by those who dedicate their lives to these problems.

I'll tell you what I did, what others have done and *are doing* and let *you* decide. Mostly, I want to make you aware of the DANGERS that we cannot see! This book is aptly named; THE SILENT KILLERS.

Pete Billac

TABLE OF CONTENTS

PART I

PART II

People don't care what you KNOW,
until they know that you CARE.

PART I
Chapter 1
THINGS IN YOUR HOUSE

The first question you might ask is, *"What IS all that 'stuff' that causes polluted air inside my own house, WHERE is it and how SERIOUS is it?"*

First off, 80 percent of what's inside your house is *dead human skin,* and the rest isn't any better. There are also DUST MITES *throughout* your home and a single ounce of dust supports FORTY-TWO THOUSAND of them!

Airborne dust mites constantly eat and excrete! They cause allergies, ear, eye and nose infections, asthma attacks, fatigue and depression.

The worst part—the reason most people do nothing about this problem—is because if they can't *see* it, *hear* it, *feel* it or *smell* it, there IS no problem. That makes sense to me.

Let's start small, like with a 1,500 square foot home which can generate FORTY POUNDS of dust annually. This computes (at one ounce of dust times 42,000 dust mites and 16 ounces to the pound, times 40 pounds of dust) to almost 27 MILLION dust mites!

**Even though you need a microscope to see
ONE of these nasty little critters,
they are there. There's more.**

BACTERIA live in your kitchen sink, behind and on your counter top, range, in your refrigerator, bathroom, in your heating and cooling system, on the floor, *in your bed* and everywhere else in your home.

MOLD SPORES are found in heating and air-conditioning systems, in damp clothing, carpet and drapes, wet sheet rock, in basements, under the house, in bathrooms and in kitchens.

**Mold spores can cause asthma
attacks, allergies, sinus headaches,
irritability and depression**.

That *great smell* from new carpets, drapes, upholstery and furniture is pleasing, isn't it? Well, what that "pleasing smell" *really* is, is chemical fumes and noxious gases that are permeating everything they come into contact with.

On construction sites (new or remodeled homes for instance) paints, plywood and particle board from cabinets, counter tops and paneling emit chemical fumes, noxious gases and odors.

Even furniture *polish*, ammonia and other cleaning products used in the home produce harmful chemical vapors and harsh fumes.

Your heating and cooling system gathers dust and moisture. Duct work is a *natural breeding ground* for mold, fungi, bacteria and dust mites. Duct work helps DISTRIBUTE these indoor air pollutants throughout your home and office.

What you bring inside on your *shoes* counts too, as well as the shoes of everyone who comes through your door. And if you have animals that come inside the home, what are THEY bringing in with them? Can you see where all of this might cause a problem?

SOME FACTS

A person spends about 90% of their time indoors and the air INSIDE the home is four to five times *more polluted* than is the OUTSIDE air. I certainly wouldn't have believed that, but I believe the facts as I researched them.

Statistics say that you spend about one-third of your living hours on earth in bed. Experts say that between two and ten *million* dust mites live in your mattress and *another* two or so million in your pillow! A 6-year-old pillow can get one-tenth of its weight from live dust mites, *dead* dust mites, dust mite *body parts* and dust mite *feces*. Ugh!

Every time you make the bed or fluff the pillow, an invisible and unhealthy cloud of *feces,* dust mites eating *dead skin* and mite *body parts* circulate through the house.

Not a pleasant thought. Makes you want to take a *baseball bat* and beat the mattress and pillow before lying down.

More than 64,000 people in major American Cities are dying *annually* from lung or heart problems. Many of these deaths, experts say, are *caused* or aggravated *by* breathing the gritty INDOOR air pollution known as *particulates.*

These microscopic particles are considered by health experts to be the deadliest air pollutant, yet this is the *first time* anyone has tried to *quantify* the threat nationally and from city to city.

The *Natural Resources Defense Council* states, *"Cardiopulmonary deaths from particulates exceed the toll from AUTO ACCIDENTS, from AIDS and from BREAST CANCER combined!"*

The group used *Harvard, American Cancer Society* research and *Environmental Protection Agency* pollution statistics to make its estimate.

"Scientists, not associated with the group's project, stated the death calculations as reasonable (even conservative) based on their own research. They used assumptions that would not give them extreme highs.

In fact, they used ones that would maybe bias it a little *downward,*" said *C. Arden Pope*, a *Brigham Young University* epidemiologist.

Each day there are reports on the TV, in newspapers and over the radio about a house or school that had to be *evacuated* and either torn down or gutted to get to these problems caused by indoor polluted air. Many *insurance companies* are *excluding* mold and mildew from their policies.

There are tiny pieces of pollution that spew from diesel trucks, cars, dusty roads, power plants and an array of other sources that are small enough to lodge in your lungs and aggravate respiratory and heart diseases.

In recent research led by the *Harvard School of Public Health, Pope* and other scientists concluded after tracking the health of thousands of people in six cities that "particulates" *shorten lives by one to three years.*

Other than the danger to your children whose immune system is not fully developed, the *biggest* risk faces the elderly and people afflicted with asthma, angina, pneumonia or other lung and heart ailments.

In numbers of deaths linked to *particulates,* the Los Angeles-Long Beach area led the nation with nearly 6,000 followed by New York, Chicago and Philadelphia.

Taking the most conservative fatality rate found in the *Harvard-American Cancer Society* study, this environmental group blamed the particulate pollution for 6.5 percent of the 980,000 annual deaths from pulmonary and heart ailments in the studied cities.

That calculates to nearly 70,000 deaths in these cities alone that are linked DIRECTLY to "polluted air!"

To carry this one step further, and if we can calculate what the experts say about INDOOR polluted air being four to five times *greater* than OUTDOOR polluted air, this means that between 56,000 and 58,000 of these deaths is because of the polluted air INDOORS!

Pope calls these death toll estimates *"quite large"* compared with other health threats. For example, the mortality estimated from *particulates* in greater Los Angeles is *four times* HIGHER than the number who died from auto accidents.

The study came as the Clinton administration was debating how to revise the EPA's nine-year-old health standard for *particulates*.

What happens and the reason why many don't concern themselves with this *problem* is because it's not like a fire, or an auto accident, or a drive-by shooting where you VIEW the person's death; this is an INVISIBLE enemy!

Several recent scientific studies have indicated the EPA's current standard is not stringent enough to safeguard health. The EPA had a court order to revise this in the near future. If something was done, I hadn't heard of it.

SCARE TACTICS OR FACT

If this frightens you a little, it certainly *should*. The more I researched this problem the more concerned I became. When I "stumbled" on a remedy I couldn't WAIT to write about it.

I don't work for any company nor am I involved with a government agency that deals with air pollution. I just write books. After learning how SERIOUS this was I came up with a rather *ominous* title hoping to "get your attention" written in plain words backed by scientific documentation.

These FACTS from different environmental agencies, from studies at *Harvard,* reports by *Peter Jennings* and a segment of *60 MINUTES,* aren't kidding you.

And, as far as *anyone else* taking care of this FOR you—NO CHANCE! If this problem exists in your own home, you can't *afford* to wait for congress to vote on it, **YOU** have to do something about it.

HOW DID THIS HAPPEN?

HOW all of this began, in the simplest of terms, is a *predictable consequence* of an ever-growing population. In the U.S. this problem was accelerated in the 1970's with the need to *conserve energy*. It seemed, at the time, like a good plan.

Due to the *Arab Oil Embargo* in the early 1980's this forced the construction industry to build homes and buildings that made saving energy a top priority. And they did.

New houses, schools, office buildings and even factories were insulated and tightly sealed. They wanted to keep the cool air inside in summer and the hot air inside in winter.

This did, in fact, save energy but it also *trapped* more pollutants INSIDE and created a breeding ground, a sort of incubator, for these deadly pollutants.

Tightly constructed buildings can't breathe and very little outside air enters. This, conversely, means that very little air that is INSIDE, can get OUTSIDE. To get fresh air inside some of these new office buildings you need to drive a FORK LIFT through a window.

It's really too late to stick culpability on anyone. Most of us don't really care who or what *caused* it, we just want it GONE! We want to know what *we* can do about this to protect ourselves and our loved ones.

The federal government has groups studying the problem and several agencies warning people, but it really is up to US to do something about it. NO, we really can't afford to wait for legislation.

DO THIS TEST IN YOUR HOME OR OFFICE

Look from inside OUT of your window on a sunny day and you'll *see* the dust *floating* in the air. This is one of the problems; you are breathing IN this floating dust and it, too, is then **trapped.** But NOW it's trapped ***inside your body!***

We can oftentimes *see* the air *outside* and it looks so bad it's smart to not breathe it for any length of time. When you LOOK at this you have to wonder, *"How can the INSIDE air be worse?"* More often than not, it is.

If your indoor air is merely *re-circulated,* the pollutants INSIDE continue to build. All the pollutants I mentioned before are being brought into the house and *trapped!* Recent studies show the danger of this trapping effect.

If ONE person sheds millions of flakes of skin each day that dust mites thrive on, think of an office building that *hundreds* of people frequent. Think of the hundreds of pairs of shoes that "stuff" is brought in clinging to the soles.

And what about the toxic *cleaning materials* used in these buildings, and when something is freshly painted, new carpet put in, new furniture replacing old furniture?

IS OUTSIDE AIR CLEANER?

That is a toss up and depends on *where* you live. If you are in Allentown, PA or Houston, TX it doesn't seem likely that inside air can be more contaminated than this OUTSIDE mess.

I've flown over major cities where you had to *cut* through layers of "stuff" that was hovering over tall buildings. There is NO WAY that the air *inside* my house is messier than this! I can SEE this outside "debris" in the air just floating—different colors even—hanging in clouds. I can SMELL it.

Certainly in areas where there are factories, or big cities with hundreds of thousands of cars spewing exhaust fumes, or on subways or busses where smokers are breathing all over you, it is MORE of a problem being outside, isn't it?

Not quite! Americans spend *90% of their time* **indoors** breathing this *noxious soup* of contaminates. In a typical home or office dust floats in the air and toxins and dirt become *trapped* in the carpet and can't get out!

Doctors advise us that dust is the last great medium of human infection. Germs have no means of locomotion except to *attach themselves* to particles of dust. We need to bring this dust to the FLOOR and kill any contaminates IN this dust.

Experts warn that various fumes of cleaning products can cause *learning disabilities*. There are actual cases of people who have been *poisoned* in their own homes.

It is estimated that a homemaker is only 30% efficient in cleaning because of dust *stirring up* and moving from room to room. A sofa CHAIR contains residue from every person that has ever sat on it. Who was there *before* you?

The ceiling—styrene, fiberglass and wood are all porous material and convenient places for accumulation of disease-causing pollution.

What about a ceiling fan? Doesn't this help? I like them; I have one in almost every room in my house. But these fans don't ELIMINATE dust. They sort of act like an *equal-opportunity employer*. They SCATTER dust in every direction, but don't do a single thing to help *eliminate* dust. Did you know that . . .

Only 10% of colds are caught outdoors; 90% are caught indoors

Remember how grandma made certain you had your collar tight, your coat buttoned to the neck, jacket zipped up and that you had your scarf with you? *"Keep your neck warm or you'll catch your death of cold,"* I remember mine saying.

And my mother (who got it from *Gran*), *"Put your shoes on. Wrap yourself tight. It's cold (or wet outside) and you'll get pneumonia."*

Nobody knew, then, that the *real* danger was INSIDE! The fact is, most STILL don't know!

The way it was explained to me is that nature *destroys* germs on dust *outdoors*, but our energy-efficient homes keep nature *out* and germs *in*. Is this starting to make some sense to you? Let's go at it from this way.

While inside your home, if you make that test and look through a ray of sunshine, 80% of what you would see is *dead skin of people that have been in this room.* Is THIS what you want to be breathing?

The *odor-generating products* and the contaminates in your house are being breathed *in* by you and your family over and over again! You need a way to get this dust down on the floor where you can't breathe it and to KILL whatever contaminates are in that dust. Also, something that gets rid of mold, mildew and bacteria.

"INDOOR AIR POLLUTION is America's most serious environmental problem affecting the health of humans"
                              EPA (Environmental Protection Agency)

There IS a way to be energy conservative and still be healthy. I'll give you a few answers. Read what these experts say! Listen to them! Many have dedicated their life researching this problem.

Woefully, there are many people in this world who will *not* listen to reasoning no matter how sound it is. They just won't go for the idea of

INDOOR air being *contaminated*. Their houses are spotless.

Far too many *wait* for problems because they can't SEE them. Only *when* it happens to them or a loved one do they look for a cure. Let's prevent this from happening. Let's get these things *before* they cause any harm.

The studies I've listed are by experts in their respective fields. They aren't trying to frighten you, only to *inform* you of their findings. I'm relaying their messages to you in simple terms.

Over and over I say: *"People don't mind getting old (that's better than the other alternative —death), but they want to grow old PAIN FREE!"*

Yes, SOME might feel that this INSIDE air pollution business and those *little critters* crawling around our bed and pillows is nothing to worry about. Well it's time we *did* worry about it! What CAN be done about this problem?

Do we *decontaminate* ourselves before we come inside so our clothing won't drag in the pollens, oils from smoke, gases, allergens and odors? Do we get dipped in some solution before we bring these outside contaminates inside?

One guy from a city agency, during a radio interview I was doing on my book, confronted me about not going after a *cure* and just treating the *symptoms*. Gosh! He's comparing me to a *medical* doctor; that's what *they* do.

His solution was that when we get water behind our tub or our sink or kitchen cabinets we have to GET THAT WATER OUT within 24 hours. "*That*," he says, "*will **prevent** the mold and mildew from forming*." He's *right*! But how can *that* be done?

Does he suggest we *tear out* our bath and shower wall after each shower and mop up the water? Do we do the same with the counter tops and sink in our kitchen—DAILY? But, he had a certificate of some kind where he attended some classes. What a TERRIFIC idea! I want to talk with his *teacher*!

～～～～～～～～

My thoughts were, while looking into this problem and searching for a solution, that if we can put people on the MOON we can certainly find a way to prevent or kill these harmful bacteria and viruses immediately before they do harm; we have genius minds in this country.

We can't tear millions of homes down and rebuild them? We can't walk around with a protec-

tive *suit* like our space travelers? We can't live in
a bubble? What IS the answer?

This next chapter will answer many of your
questions and help you understand what *won't*
work. Then, I'll tell you what will.

Chapter 2
QUESTIONS AND ANSWERS

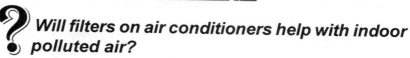 *Will filters on air conditioners help with indoor polluted air?*

NO! The fact is that *filters* on your air-conditioning unit are for the *unit itself*. It keeps the DIRT from clogging up your air-conditioning UNIT, nothing more. Dust doesn't travel *sideways*, just up and down. The ONLY dust your air conditioner filter catches is that DIRECTLY in front of the unit.

That fiberglass filter that you buy from Wal☆Mart for a buck thirty-five is to extend the life of your AIR CONDITIONER and they have to be changed, in many instances, MONTHLY.

It is from difficult to impossible for this filter to reach the air that is TRAPPED in your furniture, upholstery, drapes or carpet. These glass fiber filters regulate the AIR FLOW and some pollutants are trapped but most simply pass through into your air conditioner and heating system duct work.

And THAT is when it meets the dust, the mold and the moisture. THAT'S where most of the trouble begins. These filters develop "flow patterns" and the "non-flow" areas go untreated.

? *How about the new HIGH EFFICIENCY filters?*

These aren't NEW! They do, however, trap a higher percentage of the particles. But the effectiveness of these HEPAs is quoted by weight. Since most particles and **all** molecules are sub-micron in size, this component of bad air passes right through. Also, HEPAs are expensive, they must be changed often and they slow down the air flow.

? *I heard about ELECTRONIC air cleaners. What do you know about those?*

SOME. I know that air passes through a section where the electrically-charged plates attract the *particulates*. These filters are better than the ones above. But they too, must be changed or cleaned often, they cost a lot more and when they get clogged the air flow is stopped considerably which puts a strain on your blower motor and compressor.

THERE ARE THREE WAYS TO CLEAN INSIDE AIR:

OXIDATION
DISINFECTION
PARTICULATE CONTROL

 Can't I get rid of this dust with a good vacuum cleaner? And what is this "floating" house dust you talk about?

NO! A vacuum cleaner gets the dust from the carpet that is ON THE FLOOR! And not even a powerful vacuum cleaner gets all of the dust—not even *enough* of it.

"Floating" house dust is everywhere. It gathers in balls, hides in ducts, finds ways to "seep" in cracks between the carpet and the wall, under sofa pillows and bothers the heck out of us. We breathe dust constantly and when we sneeze we blame it on the *outside* pollen. Whereas, the majority of the time, it's the dust INSIDE.

What IS the answer? What can we do?

STUDIES SAY the answer lies with *INDOOR OZONATION!* You see, air INDOORS has less ozone than air OUTDOORS because no sun rays, no lightning bolts, waves, or waterfalls exist indoors. So, *some* way, we have to *capture the* *ozone* and move it INDOORS. Now, let's get a *bit* technical.

The earth recycles her assets in many ways. One system for converting *organic waste* into fresh resources involves OZONE, the same oxygen variant that blocks UV rays in the upper atmosphere. Closer-to-home, ozone reduces dead organic matter into carbon dioxide, water vapor and oxygen. Nature is remarkable!

 Can you tell me more about ozone so I might better understand it?

CERTAINLY! This answer is LONGER than my introduction and should tell you everything you need to know about ozone. The ***mis****understanding* about ozone is based on its confusion with pollution. *Teachers* and *scientists* who retired twenty or so years ago preached the danger of ozone while *"the jury was still out."* Their students "carried" this misinformation along with them.

I'm not "putting them down" (teachers, retired scientists *or* students) its just that there are *new* tests and *more recent* research.

My PARENTS had me eat the most UN-HEALTHY food known to mankind because *they didn't know*. The *jury was still out* then on foods also but times and science have *changed.*

NOW, there are so many different pollutants (some 3,600 in cigarette smoke alone), that it's difficult *and* expensive to measure each one. It is far easier to measure the *ozone,* nature's response to the pollution. Most weathermen announce the *degree of pollution* in terms of **ozone**.

Ozone is easy to monitor, but it is merely an *index* to the real pollution. An appropriate analogy would be the relationship of the white cell count in blood to infection. The white cell count is determined by the amount of *infection* present, but it is there to *fight* the infection. It's the same with ozone. With high pollution levels, more ozone is formed, but that ozone is working to break *down* the pollutants.

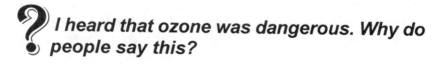 *I heard that ozone was dangerous. Why do people say this?*

Eating APPLES is dangerous—IF you eat 50 apples! Those who really don't know about ozone and only *heard* that it was dangerous are the *"sign carriers"* who march against most things. But, there will always be conflicting opinions on just about everything.

I can't *duel* with any of these non-believers

because I'm not a scientist; I just *"research the researchers."* But, I have enough evidence from well respected scientists, chemists and various research and study groups to satisfy me.

It's just common sense when you think about it. There are "ozone machines" that have been around for a decade or two with NO negative results. One company sold well over 4 MILLION of these machines without a SINGLE problem as far as emitting too much ozone.

Bet on it, that with these *"watchdog agencies,"* one slip and your company is closed forever and with news agencies, you would HEAR about it on FOX, MSNBC, CNN and every local station in existence—including IMUS—for DAYS!.

The next time someone expresses concern about the safety of ozone ask them, **"*Would you want to breathe a gas that in certain concentrations causes cramps, nausea, dizziness, hypothermia, ambylopia, respiratory difficulties. bradycardia, fainting spells and convulsions capable of leading to death?"***

When they reply *"No,"* tell them that these symptoms (whatever SOME of them *are*) result from breathing simple **OXYGEN** (O_2) in concentrations. Anything (including oxygen *and* ozone) can be undesirable at high levels.

One can drown in *too much* water. So, should *water* not be allowed indoors since people drown in it? Nonsense! We have a faucet which controls the *amount* we use. Likewise, if we have a method that can **control** the ozone level, *that* makes *it* safe also.

OZONE IS FOUND THROUGHOUT NATURE

The ozone layer in the *upper* atmosphere is created by the interaction of sunlight (UV rays) with oxygen (O_2), and protects us from harmful ultraviolet radiation. Ozone is also created in the *lower* atmosphere.

Lightning in thunderstorms split oxygen molecules leading to higher than usual concentrations of ozone bringing about that *fresh, clean smell* after a rainstorm. You needn't be a chemist or weatherman to understand it. However it, too, is a *bit* technical.

Everyday sunlight splits some of the O_2 molecules into single oxygen atoms, which then attach themselves to other O_2 molecules, creating ozone (O_3). This is an *unstable bond* and when the O_3 molecules contact pollutants the single oxygen atom attaches, thus *oxidizing* them. *This is good.*

Chemicals begin to break down the molecular bond of that molecule and *if* there is *enough* ozone it will eventually d*estroy* that molecule's bond completely, thus neutralizing it. All organic chemicals are broken down eventually into water vapor, carbon dioxide, oxygen and a few other basic molecules.

Automobile exhaust and *industrial plant emissions*, for instance, are the two principle sources of *smog*. A photochemical reaction takes place when these emissions (sunlight, moisture and heat) combine in the right set of circumstances.

A single oxygen atom is removed which then combines with atmospheric oxygen to form ozone. The ozone is reported as the "smog level."

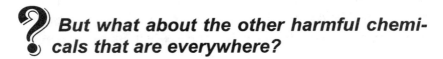 *But what about the other harmful chemicals that are everywhere?*

SMART question! The fact is we don't *hear about* the combination of various harmful compounds such as *nitrogen dioxide, nitric acid, nitrous oxide, sulfur dioxide, sulfuric acid, carbonic acid* and *carbon monoxide*. And most people (like me) wouldn't know what we were hearing anyway. But these are the *real* pollutants.

Naturally-occurring ozone is colorless, not

the grayish-brown color that is associated with smog! When there is a high level of pollution, more ozone is formed, but that ozone is working to break *down* these harmful chemicals.

Ozone is a *natural disinfectant* which reduces *bacteria, yeast, mold* and *fungi*. Natural ozone (found outside) in parts per million of .02 to .05 keeps outside air healthy.

A giant breakthrough came about when a man working in his basement invented a machine that keeps the ozone level in your home to LESS THAN point oh six (.06). It takes POINT six **(.6)**, or TEN times as much ozone to harm humans.

Ozone interacts with moisture (humidity) and makes small amounts of hydrogen peroxide, **also a disinfectant.** Thus, if we can bring this ozone INSIDE, and we can control the "dosage", we have a *double* disinfectant. Ozone is nature's BEST oxidizer (other than fire).

 Isn't fire the BEST way to oxidize?

YES it is, and another good question; you must be a chemist or an engineer. Here is what happens with fire.

Epidemics, for example, can be stopped by BURNING the homes and possessions of infected people—even the people themselves. SMELL can be destroyed through burning. This is OXIDATION at its extreme.

But, we can't start a fire INSIDE and burn our homes down. The next two paragraphs are not pleasant and perhaps a bit "graphic," but they will get the point across that will make it hard to forget.

Let's suppose you throw a *dead rat* in a fire. EVERYTHING burns; fur, flesh, entrails, bones *and* the rat all go up in smoke. The rat-burning example is what is known as conversion via oxidation, the results being carbon dioxide, water vapor, heat and a little ash.

WITHOUT the fire the rat decays in a few weeks and the smell (outdoors) fades in a matter of days. If that rat (or a mouse) was poisoned INDOORS and died in your *attic*, the smell would drive you OUTSIDE. That's because as an oxidizer, oxygen is less powerful than the (outside) ozone. This is OXIDATION. Whether by fire or ozone, oxidation REDUCES many *organics* to their sub-components.

I WARNED you this would be a long answer. But I want clarity for layman—even chemists, scientists and engineers.

UNDERSTANDING OZONE EVEN MORE

Part of what I'm going to tell you I learned from **60 Minutes**. They report on *any* and *every* problem that affects us. Their research is extensive and flawless. It makes for a good program, their ratings stay high and they tell us some things in plain language that we can understand.

More of what I learned came right out of the encyclopedia, from *Farm & Ranch* magazine, from the *Florida Fruit Growers Association*, from a packing house in Wisconsin that I forgot the name of and from scientists who study it. These sources all gave me more knowledge about ozone.

Ozone turns out to be a most effective *killer of germs*. When fruit is picked from the trees it is sometimes infected with bacteria, mold and pesticides. For decades American packers have washed food in *chlorine* but it doesn't clean away *everything* and it leaves a chemical residue. They want a *better* method. They now use **ozone.**

Can you recall how fresh the air smells after a thunderstorm? That's partly because lightning cutting through the air turns oxygen molecules (O_2) into *ozone*, which chemists label O_3.

Ozone generators are what food companies use to clean vegetables, beef and chicken. It's simple yet effective. They use *high voltage electricity* (similar to lightning) to combine the O_2 (oxygen molecules) into ozone. That ozone gas is pumped into the packing plants' water which is sprayed on the fruits.

Ozone cleans all sorts of chemicals OFF food. It kills *ECOLI, Salmonella* and *bacteria.* And there is a bonus, because the water is now recyclable *after* the wash and is pumped back *to* the ozone generator to repeat the process.

After the "vegetable water" has been filtered and treated with ozone it is beautifully clean again, ready to be used another time—and another.

The FDA approved ozone as safe in June of 1999, but cleaning with ozone is not new; Japan and Europe have been using it for decades. But the cleaning of food in the United States got little notice until recent episodes of contamination.

Plant managers say that ozone cleaning is no more expensive than chlorine and it leaves *no chemicals behind.* Plus, ozone quickly turns back into regular oxygen.

As technology spreads it could mean a safer food supply for a worried public which brings us back to our homes and our INDOOR polluted air.

Whew! I apologize. You asked what time it was

and I tell you how to BUILD a watch! However, ozone is so important in our living healthy lives that it will probably come up again later in this book. In fact, I'm certain it will. Don't bet against me; I'm writing the book.

 So, if I find out how to make my HOME safe, what about while I'm at work?

I can't answer that! Only the owner of your company or office manager can. This is a problem that requires some in-depth research on **SICK BUILDING SYNDROME**, something ELSE we can't see, hear, or smell.

The term, *Sick Building Syndrome* means that a building has either faulty air conditioning, leaky or dirty ducts, fiberglass that is exposed, NO AIR or even something '"mysterious" that makes the building unsafe for humans.

Any building MUST have air flowing, just like a fish tank has to have oxygenated water. If you dump too many chemicals or too much food *in* the tank, it is going to sour and the fish will begin floating to the top. With a *sick building* that is exactly what happens.

"*Architects began to design buildings with windows that didn't open, or sometimes even windowless. This lack of ventilation allows fungus to flourish and cause many of these buildings to become sick,"* reported *Texas Tech* researchers headed by microbiologist *David Straus.*

"At first researchers thought carpet cleaner or dusting chemicals were to blame, but for years other scientists suspected that fungus might be the culprit.

"One of the problems has been **getting owners of buildings to allow researchers to TEST for fungus.** *Many building owners are fearful of lawsuits and/ or the cost to purify the air.*

"This is the first study to achieve statistical significance by actually testing dozens of buildings," said Straus.

He and his research team were able to gain access to the school buildings because of a relationship with a Dallas company that maintains air quality for schools in Texas.

Researchers believe that through *control of the electrical charges* in the air we breathe, our moods, energy and health can be markedly improved. They have found a significant cause of *Sick Building Syndrome*, blamed for causing office workers and school children to develop hay fever-like symptoms over the past decade.

The study, published in the September 1999

edition of the *British Journal of Occupational and Environmental Medicine,* looked at 48 school buildings. They found that two types of fungus were common to them all—*Penicillium* and *Stachybotrys.*

"*Buildings in which Penicillium has become dominant in the air will cause people to experience allergic reactions,*" he said. "*Stachybotrys has toxins that cause toxic reactions.*"

Straus said the Texas Tech study should help identify whether buildings where people complain of headaches, watery eyes and respiratory problems actually *have* sick building syndrome and help to determine when the problem has been corrected. Once the fungi is eliminated from the air by increasing ventilation and eliminating standing water, the symptoms stop.

Stachybotrys is a **deadly fungus** believed to be responsible for the deaths of six children in Cleveland in 1989. Doctors never conclusively proved *Stachybotrys* was to blame, but many think that the fungus caused the children to have a toxic reaction so severe that it caused their capillaries throughout their body to burst. They are thought to have *choked to death on their own blood!*

Straus said that even though his team of researchers never detected enough of the fungus in the school buildings they studied to pose a mortal threat, they were *extremely concerned* when they found that *Stachybotrys* was involved.

"At first we thought Penicillium might be the only fungus involved, but that wouldn't explain some of the neurological symptoms some people reported, like dizziness and double vision.

"We found that those symptoms are toxic reactions to Stachybotrys, which is an entirely different kind of beast. It's much more dangerous and thrives in damp places."

World Health Organization spokesman *Dan Epstein* said other studies are focusing on whether sick building syndrome might be caused by carpet glue or binding chemicals used to install floors.

Since air is so vital, shouldn't it be clean?

YES! IT SHOULD BE! Stale or polluted air is unhealthy and causes major problems for many. According to the EPA, there are three solutions:

✔ Eliminate all sources of pollution.

This is not entirely *practical* since you and your family still have to live or work there. It's about the same as that *nincompoop* suggested we do by getting rid of water within 24 hours.

✔ Increase ventilation.

But what if the air you bring *in* is not fresh? If you live near a city or factory, it might not be. And did you know that on the *best ventilation systems* only ⅓ of the air is exchanged? Moreover, this becomes costly during the heating or cooling seasons.

✔ Filter and reuse the air.

Great idea! But, how do you *do* this? This method can be truly **in**effective since only 10% of the air in a home ever gets circulated *through* a filter. Literally, you would need *dozens* of filters in your home to make a difference.

? *So, what IS the solution? You've convinced us that the air is polluted and we want it to be clean? Do we get sprayed like fruit and vegetables with ozoneated water?*

Cute question. The ANSWER: follow the way NATURE cleans the air? For instance, the sun puts off electric charges that change some *particulates* in the air to a *negative* charge. These negative charges are attracted to the existing *positive* charges, and when these particles *join,* they become heavy and cannot stay airborne. The sun's rays also create *low-level ozone.*

As nature's most potent oxidizing agent (ozone) completes nature's process to reducing contaminates to harmless natural substances, we've found a way to put *nature* into our homes.

 ## What about *SWAMP COOLERS?*

As many miles as I've traveled and as much research as I've done, I had NEVER run across this system of cooling air until a new friend told me about them.

Swamp coolers are mostly for DRY climates, and use LESS electricity than a standard air conditioner. Experts say these cooling devices TRAP moisture and this tends to *accelerate* the accumulation of mold and mildew.

They add that there is a reservoir in this cooling system and the water in that reservoir can also cause problems.

Chapter 3
UNDERSTANDING CLEAN AIR

I compliment those of you who have gotten this far into this book. Yet, even though you're bright, it doesn't necessarily mean that this particular side of your brain *understands* scientific jargon or that you even care to read about it.

I, as a person whose mind doesn't think in these areas (or care) put much of this in for those of you who *do* understand and who *do* care.

To me, it's like an air conditioner; I could care less that it has refrigerant, a filter, compressor, condenser or whatever. I don't care **how** it works, I just want to touch a button and have it COOL me! But, I can't know EVERYTHING and if it doesn't interest me, I could NEVER learn it.

This is some information on **NATURAL FRESH AIR.** It contains three ingredients normally ABSENT from indoor air. To clean our INSIDE air of pollutants we must have all of the following:

1. *An electrical charge (ionization).*
2. *Small quantities of ozone (O_3).*
3. **Adequate air circulation.**

Equipment using these processes has achieved 80% **reductions** in mold, mildew, bacteria and help *control particulates*. Also, dust mites *do not thrive* where ozone is present. Most people would agree with these statements, except for the word "ozone."

IONS AND IONIZATION

One sweltering day in Philadelphia this summer a man sat before a small metal box resting atop a hospital file cabinet. It was plugged into an ordinary wall socket. A doctor flipped a switch. Inside the box a small fan whirred, the box hummed distantly like a high-tension wire and gave off a faint, sweetish odor. Soon the man felt alert and refreshed as though he'd been taking deep gulps of sparkling October air.

The doctor turned the machine off, then switched on another that *looked* just like it. The air grew quickly stale. The man's head felt stuffy. His eyes smarted. His head began to ache. He felt vaguely depressed and tired.

With this simple experiment, the scientist, *Dr. Igho H. Kornblueh*, of the *American Institute of Medical Climatology*, demonstrated the effect that *atmospheric ions* can have on human beings. The first machine generated *negative* ions; the second, *positive* ions.

The air around us is filled with electrically charged particles. They are generated in invisible billions by cosmic rays, radioactive elements in the soil, ultraviolet radiation, storms, waterfalls, winds, and the friction of blowing sand or dust.

Every time we draw a *breath* these ions enter our lungs. They appear to have a lot to do with such things as our moods, why cattle grow skittish before a storm, why rheumatic joints tingle when the barometer falls and how ants know in advance of oncoming rain in time to block their tunnels.

POSITIVE EFFECT OF NEGATIVE IONS

Falling barometric pressure and hot, dry, seasonal winds such as Alpine *foehn* (warm dry wind blowing down into the valleys of a mountain, especially the Alps), and the Rocky Mountain *chinook* (on the eastern slope of the Rockies, a warm, dry wind coming from the north or west) and the Pacific Coast *Santa Ana* winds for example, pack the air with an excess of *positive* ions.

Not everyone is affected; healthy *young* people swiftly adapt to the change, but countless others are distressed. The *aged* come down with respiratory complaints, aching joints, asthma sufferers wheeze and gasp, children grow cranky and perverse, crime and suicide rates climb.

On the other hand, when a preponderance of *negative* ions spices the air with exhilarating freshness, we feel *on top of the world*! There really IS something to science. I am continually amazed at how smart some people are.

Dr. C. W. Hansell, research fellow at *RCA Laboratories* and an international authority on ionization, illustrates the effect with a story about his ten-year-old daughter:

"We were outside, watching an approaching thunderstorm. I knew that clouds of negative ions were filling the air. Suddenly my daughter began to dance across the grass, a radiant look on her face. She leaped up on a low boulder, threw her arms wide to the dark sky and cried, 'I feel wonderful!'"

Negative ions *cure* nothing that we know of. At most they afford relief only so long as one inhales them. Many doctors doubt their therapeutic effects. But there is a growing army of people who swear by them. Again, a *toss up.* I try to get a greater majority of one opinion and put it in the book. I can't argue the point on either.

TOTAL RELIEF

At the *University of Pennsylvania's Graduate Hospital* and at *Northeastern* and *Frankford* hospitals in Philadelphia, *Dr. Kornblueh* and his associates have administered negative-ion treatments to hundreds of patients suffering from hay fever or bronchial asthma.

Of the total, 63% have experienced partial to total relief. "*They come in sneezing, eyes watering, noses itching, worn out from lack of sleep, so miserable they can hardly walk.*" One doctor told me that 15-minutes in front of the negative-ion machine and they felt so much better they didn't want to leave.

It was RCA's *Dr. Hansell* who, in 1932, stumbled upon the behavioral effects of artificially generated ions. He noticed a startling swing in the moods of a fellow RCA scientist who worked beside an electrostatic generator.

Some days the scientist finished work alert and in bubbling good spirits. On other days he was rude, ill-tempered and depressed. *Dr. Hansell* investigated and found that when the generator produced *negative* ions he was fine, but morose when the machine was producing *positive* ions. A few months later, reports of ionization research in

Europe confirmed the strange experience.

A few years ago *atmospheric ions* became suddenly important to *military researchers* in environmental medicine. How would they affect men locked in submarines? In space ships? What *were* the possibilities of ion therapy? Research programs multiplied with fantastic results.

AN EFFECTIVE PAINKILLER

Dr. Kornblueh studied brain-wave patterns and found evidence that negative ions *tranquilized* persons in severe pain. In one dramatic test he held a negative *ionizer* to the nose and mouth of a factory worker whom they had rushed to *Northeastern Hospital* with second-degree burns on his back and legs. In minutes the pain was gone. Morphine, customarily administered in such cases, was never necessary.

Today, *all* burn cases at *Northeastern Hospital* are immediately put in a windowless, *ion-conditioned* room. In ten minutes, usually, the pain is gone. Patients are left in the room for 30 minutes. The treatment is repeated three times every 24 hours. In 85% of the cases they need no pain-deadening narcotics.

Northeastern's Dr. Robert McGowan says,

"*Negative ions make burns dry out faster, heal faster and with less scarring. They also reduce the need for skin-grafting. They make the patient more optimistic as well as causing them to sleep better.*"

Encouraged by this success in burn therapy, *Dr. Kornblueh, Dr. J. R. Minehart, Northeastern's* chief surgeon, and his associate *Dr. T. A. David,* boldly tried negative ions in relief of deep, post-operative pain.

During an eight-month test they exposed 138 patients to negative ions on the first and second days after surgery. *Dr. Kornblueh* announced the results at a London congress of bioclimatologists. In 79 cases, *57% of the total*—negative ions eliminated or drastically reduced pain.

"*At first,*" said *Dr. Minehart,* "*I thought it was voodoo. Now, I'm convinced that it's real and revolutionary.*" Experiments by *Dr. Albert F. Krueger* and *Dr. Richard Smith* at the *University of California* have shown how ionization affects those sensitive to airborne allergens.

Our bronchial tubes and trachea (windpipe) are lined with tiny filaments called *cilia.* The *cilia* normally maintain a whip-like motion of about 900 beats a minute. Together with mucus, they keep our air passage free of dust and pollen. *Drs. Krueger* and *Smith* exposed tracheal tissue to negative ions, found that the ciliary beat was speeded *up to* 1,200 a minute and that mucus flow was increased.

Doses of *positive* ions produced the *opposite* effect, ciliary beat slowed to 600 a minute or less, and the flow of mucus dropped.

COUNTERACTING CANCER

In experiments that may prove important in cancer research, *Drs. Krueger* and *Smith* also discovered that *cigarette smoke* slows down the *cilia* and *impairs their ability* to clear foreign, and possibly carcinogenic (cancer-inducing), substances from the lungs.

Positive ions, administered along with the cigarette smoke, lowered the ciliary beat as before, but from three to ten times *faster* than in normal air. **Negative ions**, however, *counteracted* the effects of the smoke, observed *Dr. Krueger.* "*The agent in cigarette smoke that slows down the ciliary beat is not known.*"

Whatever it may be, its action is effectively neutralized by *negative ions* which raise the ciliary beat as well as in a heavy atmosphere of cigarette smoke as they do in fresh air.

MOOD ALTERATION

 How do ions trip off our moods?

Most authorities agree that ions act on our capacity to *absorb and utilize* oxygen. Negative ions in the bloodstream *accelerate* the delivery of oxygen to our cells and tissues, frequently giving us the same euphoric jolt that we get from a few whiffs of straight oxygen.

Positive ions *slow down* the delivery of oxygen, producing symptoms markedly like those in *anoxia*, or *oxygen starvation*. Researchers also believe that negative ions may stimulate the *reticulo-endothelial* system (a group of defense cells in our bodies which marshal our resistance to disease).

Dr. Krueger predicts that we will someday regulate the ion level *indoors* much as we now regulate temperature and humidity.

Ironically, today's air-conditioned buildings, trains and planes frequently become super-charged with harmful *positive ions* because the metal blowers, filters and ducts of air-conditioning systems strip the air of negative ions before it reaches its destination. This explains why so many people in air-conditioned spots feel depressed and have an urge to throw open a window.

Air conditioner manufacturers are designing new systems that *increase* negative ionization. The *American Broadcasting Co.* will equip its new 30-story New York City headquarters with ion control.

Two national concerns, *Philco* and *Emerson Electric*, already have ion-control air-conditioning systems on the market. *RCA, Westinghouse, General Electric* and *Carrier Corp.* have similar products under study and/or development. We still have much to learn about atmospheric ions.

Nevertheless, researchers believe that these magic bits of electricity, under artificial control, will soon be helping millions toward healthier, happier, more productive lives. And through control of the electrical charges in the air, our moods, energy and health can be markedly improved.

Chapter 4
THE SOLUTION

THUNDERSTORM IN A BOX

The air after a thunderstorm truly IS fresh and clean and sweet-smelling. If a thunderstorm can't get *inside* our homes to keep us well, let's BRING IN our *own* thunderstorm. **THAT is the solution!**

My research brought me to a company in Tennessee that manufactures what many believe to be *the* very BEST air purification systems in America today. Their machines *recreate nature's own air purifying process* by using ions to *sweep* contaminants from the air and thus creating ozone molecules to oxidize and eliminate pollution.

Their systems make indoor air *mountain fresh* and NOTHING is as fresh or makes us feel better than to take a deep breath of *fresh clean air.* I have FIVE of these systems that I use in my home, office, warehouse and barn.

Remember, I do not **SELL** filters, purifying units or machines. I do not **represent** nor am I being paid **by** any company or individual to hype their product. I did this research on my own and at my own expense. I'm telling you what I found out and am simply "sharing" my findings with you.

I used this air purification unit for *one single night* and IMMEDIATELY I could breathe easier. I did, in fact, feel as if I was outside breathing the clean air we smell after a thunderstorm.

WHAT EXACTLY IS IT?

It is the *personal computer*, the *telephone*, the VCR, the *microwave.* It is a revolutionary, simple, *affordable* solution to a complex, widespread problem. In hindsight, it's obvious; like using a wheel to transport a load. Great ideas are like that. Many often say, *"Why didn't I think of that?"*

Air purifying units are one of the most *needed* items in our present-day world of pollution and contaminates. A machine that will PURIFY IN-DOOR AIR is one of the world's greatest innovations. Neither I nor any of the researches I spoke with have found another way to do this.

Only the rich could afford the first televisions. Computers were once just for *nerds* and accountants. Now, few can run a business without one. The VCR was expensive and complex when it first came out. Even though most people *still* can't program them, we almost all own one.

These products were daring, "science fiction," cutting-edge and they *revolutionized our lives*. They forever changed how we travel, communicate, work, how we live and how we are entertained.

NOBODY thought they *needed* any of these things. People weren't sitting around before the car came along saying, "*I'm sick to death of riding a horse. What I **really** need is a car!*" A lot of good that would have done them anyway. There were mostly horse trails and no gasoline stations.

Well one day, in Nebraska, an inventor came up from his basement with a little wooden box with a fan in it, tucked under his arm. I had no way of knowing how that was going to change my life, bring a NEW LIFE back to my ailing son and change the lives of millions for the better. **But it DID and it HAS!**

The inventor said it would **purify** the air in our home. At that time, nobody cared! NOW, with all the sickness, allergies, people on breathing machines and with the new research and the NEWS that scares us to death, people who are in these hurtful situations DO care. *I'm* forever grateful to that man for his unique and needed invention. My family is healthy, I've written this book and I'm happy to be telling others about it.

INDOOR AIR PURIFICATION

I got the following information from a copy of *Money Makers Magazine* dated December 1996. The inventor with the wooden box, *Bill Converse*, said:

"I knew the problems associated with filtration and became intrigued with the idea of using electrical technologies to PURIFY the air the same way it's done in nature. There are no purification machines outside and there are plenty of pollutants."

His new *"oxygen* machine" *worked* and his timing was perfect. But , *Mr. Converse* was so far *ahead of his time* that almost no one knew what he was talking about. He had found a solution for a problem that most of the WORLD didn't even know existed. But as things do, when timing, genius and opportunity meet on destiny's bridge, the winds of change began to blow.

About this time, *Chronic Fatigue* and *Sick-Building Syndrome* were added to the dictionary. Indoor air quality and soaring respiratory ailments became frequent subjects of discussion in newspapers and on government panels.

As the experts began to identify the problem and search for a solution, this formally *obscure* inventor became an international authority. I finally met him face-to-face about four years *after* I had written this book. He certainly is bright, he works very hard and I **liked** him. He is a devout Christian and a good man.

His little gadget became the topic for talk show discussions. *Experts* took the box apart piece by piece, argued over its merits, taunted its claims and in the pattern of all significant innovations, they did their best to *discredit* the machine and its maker. **THEY COULDN'T DO IT!**

The "thing" was about as flashy as a *Model T* and as user-friendly as a rotary phone, *but it worked!* It worked so well that people could *smell* and *feel* the difference immediately. They told friends who told friends and now more than 4.5 million units have been sold, maybe more.

So-called experts and cynics warned that further testing was essential to prove that the new technology was *"safe for humans,"* but in reality, this inventor used nothing *new* to produce its startling results.

"In fact," says the inventor, *"we used technology as old as the earth itself. We wanted to cleanse and purify the air in your home—naturally.*

"Every time the sun comes up, every time the lightning strikes across the sky, it cleanses the

*air outside. We copied that process, 'harnessed it,' (so to speak) and brought it **inside**."*

My next step was to search for testimonials from people who USED these machines. I had MY proof. But I wanted to find out from *others* who have used them.

TESTIMONIALS

I never professed to being a good writer, but I'm one dogged RESEARCHER. And, I just *love* testimonials from people who have problems and who find an answer and are willing to share their experiences with others who have similar problems so they might "identify" with them.

Plus, these testimonials are (usually) written in words we can all understand. When another *regular* human being tells what has happened to *them* because of some medication or invention, we want to know about it. We want to have it work on *us*, too.

MY OWN TESTIMONIAL
(Why I wrote this book)

I mentioned some of this in the INTRODUCTION of this book and "touched on it" along the way, but

I want to tell you, in the words of Paul Harvey, "*The rest of the story.*"

I was giving a meeting a few years ago talking about my new book, NEW FATHER'S BABY GUIDE. I joked about how MUCH kids cost to raise and that my 5-year-old had been "down" every two months for almost four years from five to nine days with fever, sore throat, complete fatigue, and he was in pain and didn't want to move.

I took him to *specialists* around the world. He went through test after test for more than three YEARS. He was stuck with needles, cut on his fingers, blood was drawn, a series of medications were prescribed, there was a list of food he could and *couldn't* eat and yet, every two months like clockwork, he was *down*.

You NEVER know what true love is until you have children; those of you who have children know what I mean. It literally *broke my heart* to see my son in such pain. It was almost like seeing him DROWN and not be able to save him.

After that meeting a man stepped from the crowd (*Ken Harris*) and said "*Follow me to my car. I have something I feel will help your son.*" Of course I followed.

Ken gave me a wooden box half the size of a computer monitor. "*Take this home and try it.*"

Then call me." I took it home and put it on top of my television set and plugged it in, NOT the ideal placement.

My wife and I awoke in the morning with NO sinus headache. We immediately noticed how *clean* the house smelled, JUST like the air outside after a thunderstorm.

For the first time, during these Texas summers, in about TEN YEARS, we did not take pills for a sinus headache. We could only smile at each other. We *forgot* about our son for the moment.

Three days later when (like clockwork) he was due to become ill again, **it didn't happen!** Then four days, five days, a WEEK, then TWO weeks. I called Ken and bought the machine.

It's been more than four YEARS now, and my son (now nine) is CURED! He has almost forgotten about the pain he went through. I haven't forgotten. I do not want other children to hurt or other parents to go through what we did. I went on a *mission* to find out about INDOOR air pollution to write about it in this book.

Yes, I have FIVE of these machines (home, office and barn) and I gave one to my secretary whose husband has emphysema. He felt better INSTANTLY! Here is another "close to home" testimony in which some of you might identify.

OVER TWENTY YEARS OF HURT

Ty Thompson is a hard-working, friendly young man of 28 who has a carpet business here in Burnet, Texas where I have my ranch.

While visiting my office to give me a carpet bid he commented that the air smelled fresh and wanted to know why. Of course, I had an air purification unit (a *Classic*) that runs ALL the time.

"I've had trouble breathing for more than 20 years," he said. *"I've been examined by no less than thirty doctors including several top in their profession. NONE could help, only prescribe medication that costs between $600 and $800 per month.*

If I don't take this medication, I can hardly breathe or function. It affects my work and my entire life. But, being in this office for minutes, I could breathe better. My head, my eyes, my nose . . . EVERYTHING cleared up. Where can I get one of these?" he smiled, putting his hand on the *Classic*.

I put him in touch with the person who sold me my last four machines. Within two weeks his dad came in with him and ordered one for himself. Then *Ty* ordered yet ANOTHER for his carpet store. Within ONE MONTH he went off ALL medication and now SELLS air purification systems.

He also coaches my boys in soccer. Every time he sees me he smiles and runs up to shake my hand and thank me again and again for making his life happier and healthier.

SALON SHOP ODORS ELIMINATED

Thank goodness I looked over this a time or two *before* this book went to press. Actually, one of my editors caught it. I had for a beginning title:

"Salon Shop OWNER Eliminated."

"A hair salon has many chemicals and odors in the air at all times. Between the hair color, bleaches, perm solutions, hair sprays, artificial nail solvents and acrylic solutions combined it can make for an unpleasant odor as well as a serious environmental problem.

"The air purifiers have eliminated not only the odors, but have cleaned up the air so well that even our complexions are better! It's true! All of the staff has noticed cleaner, less oily complexions and best of all—fewer illnesses."

SCHOOLS USE THEM

"We have staff and students with asthma and they could FEEL the difference in their breathing immedi-

ately after we purchased air purification units. Parent's noticed the change immediately also when they visited our school.

"Children who were coughing when they were outside and in their cars, stopped coughing the instant they came into our building."

Greenwood Christian Preschool
Houston, TX

ASTHMATICS

"Because of my severe asthma, I have been using a pulmo-aide up to four times a day for several years. Since I purchased an air purifier I no longer use my pulmo-aide.

"I have prayed for better health for a long time and I truly believe that this machine is an answer to my prayers. Our entire home smells fresh and clean and I now sleep better than I have in years."

CLEANS AND FRESHENS PET HOSPITAL

"I've been a veterinarian for twenty-six years. An air purifying system took my clinic smell completely out and replaced it with healthier, oxygenated, ionized, revitalized air. My children noticed it first. They were so familiar with that animal clinic odor that they 'could smell' me coming. No more!

"My wife has allergies that numbed her nose to the air in my animal hospital. She noticed a change in the smell and could actually 'feel' of the air a short time after I had the system installed. The clinic smells so great that I bought another unit for my kennel area.

"Again, success? It has effectively controlled the odors there as well, and the air is cleaner, healthier and smells better. It has brought a cleanliness to my clinic that even the most expensive scrubs and chemicals combined with strenuous scouring could not bring. An almost odorless animal clinic is miraculous."

Centerville Animal Hospital
Lithonia, GA

A VIP TELLS HIS STORY

ED JOHNSON is an attorney. His list of credits reads like a *Who's Who* of the century. His biography appears in *Who's Who in American Law, Who's Who in the South and Southwest, Who's Who in Finance and Industry* and *Who's Who in the **WORLD!***

Ed lives in nearby San Antonio (that's TEXAS) with his gorgeous wife, Yvonne. I had planned to visit him until he told me that he had 12 CATS and that the cats lived INSIDE!

Whew! I recall my single days when I'd rather

date a woman with 12 KIDS than two CATS and especially if the cats lived INSIDE. Ed assured me that his air purifiers worked.

Reluctantly, I did visit Ed and his home smelled like a *Rose Garden*. I could NOT believe it! I became **more** of a "believer" and look forward to my next visit with my two new friends and their TWELVE cats.

Ed *knows* about indoor air pollution. In a letter to the president of *EcoQuest International*, Ed wrote:

"Dear Mr. Jackson, For about 20 years I suffered with increasing migraine headaches which progressed to cluster headaches, necessitating heavy prescription painkillers such as Codeine and others. These headaches lasted for three or four days and were so intense that I was confined to bed.

"On Thanksgiving Day, 1996, I tried one of your air purifiers and within two HOURS of turning it on, my cluster headaches were gone and have NEVER returned!

"We have twelve cats (here's those CATS again) *and three dogs, all of which live indoors in our 4,000 square foot home. Your indoor air purifiers make our home one of the best smelling homes in all of San Antonio. Friends, family and ANYONE who visits us is amazed! 'How DO you keep it smelling so clean and fresh with ALL of these animals?' And I tell them."*

DOCTOR SAYS IT'S GOOD

"I have always known the importance of clean air, clean water and good food and its effects on the human body. I became particularly interested in the technology that is used to accomplish air purification.

At first, even with my science background, it seemed too good to be true. I have to admit I was a bit skeptical. I used one in our clinic to try for just a few days. I needed to be convinced!

"I have since shared my proven value of indoor air purification with many people, and the stories I'm hearing are too numerous to account here in this letter. The need for this product is truly overwhelming."

GET RID OF THAT SMOKING DOG

We can put a man on the moon but we could not get rid of the odor on one of our dogs. I've been told that 'the only way to get rid of the dog ODOR, is to get rid of the DOG!

*"I have been a devout pipe smoker for many years and although the aroma is pleasing to me, (Yeah, like the CAT smell) others complained about it. My wife and I also have two fairly large house dogs. One has always been plagued with a rather **pungent** odor that emanates from her no matter what is done to correct it. As a result, our 2,000 square foot home always smelled like a wet dog smoking a pipe!*

"One day my wife came home with an air purifier loaned to her by a friend. My first words were 'That little thing is going to do the whole house? Yeah, sure.'

"Well, much to our amazement, our house was totally odorless within a couple of hours! Not long after, my wife was able to discontinue her allergy medication for the first time in many years. We could no longer see dust floating in the air, the air seemed lighter and easier to breathe and a multitude of other benefits were noticed."

LEIA & MARK RYAN of Goodhue, Minnesota think so much of *their* air purification machines that they wrote *Mr. Converse* (the inventor), and to the president of the company where they bought their air purification machines:

"Just a quick note on how wonderful your air purifiers are. They do more than just take care of odors from smoke, cooking, paint and new carpet but ALSO from our basement and the odor smell of mold and mildew.

"There is NEVER that unpleasant odor any more. I also use it to clean up my car when the humidity is high, it takes the dust from my home and my husband sleeps through the night when the pollen season is at its prime. Our lives truly ARE more satisfying because of your machines. Thank you both."

HAIR AND NAIL SALON

"In our hair and nail salon we have a lot of different smells including perms and nail products. On busy days sometimes the smells can knock your socks off! A salesperson was nice enough to let us try a purification machine for a few days.

What a difference! Our place of business is clean and fresh-smelling all day, we have never had this result from anything else we had tried."

COUGHING AND ASTHMA

"My daughter is almost five years old. Since birth she has coughed every night. The cough sounded as if she had pneumonia or a deep chest cold. A few days after using this 'magic box' she stopped coughing.

"Being skeptical, we waited a few more nights but the cough was gone. It's been almost two months now and only once has she coughed (she had a cold). Since birth we have had her into the doctor numerous times with no solution.

"My wife has asthma. Many times I have taken her to the emergency room because of it. Since I bought an indoor air purifier, she has not used her atomizer with the frequency she had to use it before.

"Our entire family now wakes up in the morning with clear breathing. Especially in this colder weather when stuffy noses due to the drier air are prevalent."

CIGAR SMOKE GONE

"We were on the verge of installing a major system in our grill to clean up the cigar smoke odor, but an air purifying system has proven very effective for this purpose. Its compact size and quiet operation is exactly what we needed."

Director of Operations
The Ritz-Carlton
Phoenix, AZ

FOOTBALL LOCKER ROOM

*"I am the football equipment manager at the University of North Carolina and in charge of general maintenance of our locker room. We purchased several air purifier units last summer and have noticed a **major improvement** in the locker room smell and atmosphere. The number of colds and general illnesses on our football team have decreased also.*

"We have been especially pleased with the fact that these units produce fresh, clean-smelling air without creating their own strong odor."

AUTO EXHAUST

"Our drive-in banks were plagued with bad odors caused by the automobiles of customers. The intro-

duction of air purification units into our branch banks has had a remarkable effect on the air quality, and our employees have all been pleased with the change. We recommend this technology."

FOR ALLERGIES

"Since December 1991 I've used air purifiers with many of our patients who suffer from severe upper respiratory allergies. Most suffer from house dust, pollen, dander, mold, mildew and many chemical compounds. In every case, the patients have responded with almost no new indoor attacks.

"These machines are excellent for removing the various allergens from the indoor environment, thereby alleviating allergic reactions. Those with asthma do well on low settings.

"The most gratifying experience was when I loaned one to a patient referred by Dr. Foster Montalbano, M.D. This patient had severe allergies and she was allowed to use the machine for a few days. She later bought the machine and responded in a letter that said, 'I LOVE IT! I LOVE IT! I will never give it up! Thank you for this wonderful purifier'."

CAT URINE SMELL ELIMINATED

*"I wanted to sell my house, BUT a very strong **tears-in-the-eyes** cat urine odor was present during certain*

atmospheric conditions. I tried industrial strength odor-neutralizing chemicals. I replaced drywall sections, sealed and painted walls with odor/stain paint, cleaned and sealed the floors, replaced carpet tack strips, even took away the animal. NONE OF THIS WORKED!

"The **first** test was after four days of localized placement of the air purifier in known problem spots and centralized treatment by floor levels in this 2,000 square foot split-level house, the odor was **gone!**

"The **second** test was to determine if the odor would return **after** the removal of the machine. It DID NOT! The **third and final test** was to expose the treated house to the prospect who had placed a contingency on buying the property only if there was NO cat urine odor. We made the sale."

DON'T ACCEPT PAIN

"I have been a nutritional consultant for years. I feel and look healthy, I'm not overweight, I exercise regularly and I'm disciplined about my diet. BUT, I had ALLERGIES that caused headaches, sinus problems, even mood swings. Like many, I learned to live with it.

"At many of my lectures on health, I had to use a Kleenex for my runny nose. Every DAY I would wake up and sneeze about 20 times and being in health and nutrition for 17 years, I tried EVERYTHING!

"I found a combination of herbs and vitamins that **helped,** but I was taking TEN pills THREE TIMES *a day. I spent 90% of my time INDOORS, either at home, my office, car or the gym.*

"My boys had a six-inch pet IGUANA! It was cute when it was small, but it was now about three feet long and it SMELLED up their room and part of the upstairs. Like my allergies, we learned to live with it.

"Several friends mentioned INDOOR AIR POLLUTION. They each said that an air purifier would help and I began research on ions and ozone. I bought one and put it in my bedroom. The first WEEK my allergies improved. I asked the dealer for another week TRIAL (you can do that—test it before you buy).

The second week I was barely sneezing. I then put it in my boys' room and it took out, TOTALLY, the iguana odor in one day. My WIFE was convinced.

"Near the end of the second week my nose STOPPED running. Two of my six children had an allergy problem and they got total relief. We all SLEEP better, we all FEEL better. We've also, noticed fewer colds and less sickness around our home.

*"In fact, these air purification units helped so many that we now SELL them and thus, bring answers to many who are suffering! Our feelings are that the ONLY reason people don't have one is that they **don't know about them!"***

A.J. and Caroline Krause
Mobile, AL

DR. STAN HARRIS is a Baptist minister, a charismatic speaker, a physical fitness enthusiast and is also an 8th degree **BLACK BELT** in *Karate*. He is the Pennsylvania heavyweight *Karate* champion. We are "telephone friends." I talk with him often and I like him.

For 18 years Stan was a traveling Evangelist sometimes speaking several times a day to congregations across America. He is a firm believer in these air purifying machines. Here is what he wrote to me:

"One time I rented a NO SMOKING room but I could still smell the smoke. I've never smoked and am extremely sensitive to cigarette smoke smells. Then, some friends loaned me an air purifier to try. It was FANTASTIC! I got the best nights sleep of my life.

"I got up an hour earlier and felt good, not even jet lag. My energy level increased and I asked if I could use their air purifier for the remainder of the week. I then bought it.

"When I returned home, I put it in my basement. Within a few HOURS the fresh, clean smell replaced the musty odors, the MOLD dried up and the frequency of sickness DROPPED in our home.

"I now SELL these machines I believe in them so strongly. I help people spiritually, physically and I talk other ministers into selling these machines. This helps them financially."

IS IT SAFE?

What IS this little "magic box" that does such wonders? I call mine my **"THUNDERSTORM IN A BOX."** The machine works miracles on cleansing the indoor air that was steadily becoming more problematical and unhealthy?

It isn't large; I measured and weighed it and it's only 10 inches tall, 8 inches wide, 12 inches deep and weighs a mere 16 pounds, BUT it **purifies** the air in homes up to 3,000 square feet. This includes moldy basements, dusty attics, closets, stale vacation homes, water damaged properties, working or sleeping areas, sick buildings (offices), nursing homes, hospices, hotel and motel rooms.

From those that I've interviewed, they tell me these small wonders take out odors from smoking areas, beauty salons, barber shops, kitchens, food service areas, cafeterias, veterinary clinics, kennels, daycare centers, community rooms and meeting rooms—including SKUNK odors.

They eliminate the odors in garbage and trash areas, businesses that generate various odors, chemicals, airborne *particulates*, auto dealerships, locker rooms, fish markets, meat storage lockers and in our homes!

It is ALSO a GREAT way to get the *smoke smell* from CARS

Many used cars are NOT sold because the previous owner was a smoker. To get the smoke smell OUT would be a giant boost in sales.

WITH THE USE OF THIS MACHINES. . .

Allergic reactions are reduced
Sleeping is improved
Non-specific headaches are reduced
General environment improved
Depression reduced
Symptoms of sinus problems relieved

Yes, this "miracle machine" reactivates the INSIDE air and produces the same results as a thunderstorm does on our **outdoor environment**. With all of these obvious benefits it would seem that *everyone* would want to at least TRY this type of device.

TRY IT—FREE

The **GREAT NEWS** is that there are companies who will let you TEST their unit *before* you buy it.

If one does NOT let you TRY it to make certain it "works" on you, hang up and try another company that does.

When you find a company who believes in their product and lets you *test* it, if after several days you decide that it has done nothing for you, **send it back!** Make certain you have a written guarantee to this effect.

A reputable company will do this. They will pay the shipping. **NO** risk, **NO** expense and **NO** hassle. If you can't find a number, call ME and I'll put you in touch with a dealer near you.

Woefully, there will ALWAYS be individuals or a group who fight progress, who propagate the *myths* about the dangers of ozone and who completely ignore the wide acceptance of the *benefits* of ozone.

Don't be angry if they don't listen to you, hand them this book and hope they read it. If they are not convinced, pass them up and simply pray for them. Then say an extra prayer that they remain healthy.

COMMON SENSE

Considering the safety, the wide range and level of effectiveness, the cost of energy and the problems with our current indoor environment, the *only* alternative, it seems, is to bring clean, fresh air into our homes with a *manmade* replacement.

I found that *many* people are living with some type of respiratory problem; hay fever, allergies, sinus, headaches, *migraines* and various *breathing problems.* The sad part is that they are *content* to live this way and attribute it to "old age" never thinking that the true culprit could be the polluted air in their homes.

I can not **GUARANTEE** that an air purification unit will **CURE** you of anything. What I *can* tell you is that it was "the" answer for me, for my wife and for my son. It was for Ty, my carpet salesman friend and it was for hundreds that I interviewed.

**It's just common sense to TRY it
and SEE if it works for you.**

PART II
LET'S TALK ABOUT WATER

We MUST drink water to survive. There are cases where humans have lived for as long as three MONTHS without food, but without water it takes only THREE DAYS to begin complications and you sort of "slip" into a semi-comatose state.

LIQUIDS do not necessarily mean *water*; coffee, tea, coke, sprite, Kool-Aid and *alcohol* all *contain* water, but they cause the body to LOSE water. They are also *diuretics* and tend to create *more* dehydration. Water is necessary for LIFE.

To be healthy, experts say we should drink 64 ounces of water each day. A more *accurate* measure is to take our weight, cut that in half, divide by ten, and *drink* that many 8-ounce glasses of *toxin-free* water each day. It "flushes" or body.

Let's make it simple. If you weigh 200 pounds cut that in half; we have 100 pounds. Divide by 10 leaves 10. So drink 10, 8-ounce glasses of water each day. Another example:

If a person weighs 160 pounds, divide by two which leaves 80 pounds. Divide again by 10; 10

goes into 80, 8 times. So, drink EIGHT 8-ounce glasses of water each day.

But, if there is so much "bad stuff" in most water, what KIND of water are we talking about? I recommend PURIFIED water that has been treated by a proven water-purification system.

According to EPA studies and scientists on *Environmental Protection Agency's* advisory board, ALL agree that CONTAMINATED drinking water ranks as one of the TOP public health risks in the United States! Think about this:

MUCH of our *drinking water* in the United States contains inorganic minerals such as calcium and magnesium carbonate, toxic chemicals, and water that "passes through" *polluted air* on its way to the ground.

What does this mean? Is my water UNSAFE to drink? The answers are MAYBE and POSSIBLY. But how can this be? Who wrote this book, *Stephen King?* Next you'll tell me that the water is POISONOUS! Well, it *might* be. The following are FACTS.

Would you *intentionally* ingest a material that is used as a PESTICIDE, and has been suspected of causing cancer, hip fractures, intellectual impairment, fertility problems, dental problems—even FISH deformities?

Well, **two-thirds** of the population of the United States—and soon the **entire population** of Los Angeles and its surrounding communities—, takes this material into their bodies EVERY DAY if they use tap water in *any* way!

The use of FLUORIDE in our drinking water is listed as one of the top 25 CENSORED stories of 1998. While going over hundreds of CLASSIFIED documents about the U.S. Atomic bomb development program, the *Manhattan Project*, reporters found that FLUORIDE was the key chemical in atomic bomb production.

Yes, *fluoride* was the *top* chemical hazzard of the *U.S. Nuclear Weapons Program*, not only for those who *worked* the project but for those in nearby communities as well.

And documents showed that the first U.S. lawsuits levied against the atomic weapons program were over *FLUORIDE* poisoning, not radiation damage. I INVESTIGATED these facts!

I could write hundreds of pages on the dangers of fluoride and why it is NOT good for our teeth OR our health. The main problem is, most people don't KNOW about this, and many more don't CARE—until it happens to them—or the ones they love.

A former head of toxicology in one of America's foremost dental centers found that fluoride is a powerful CENTRAL NERVOUS SYSTEM TOXIN and that the *human brain* could be affected, *adversely,* even at low doses.

Want more information on the dangers and past horrid history of fluoride? I have books listed near the end of *this* book that you can buy to read more about it.

MY PROBLEM-SOLVED

I live on a ranch in the Texas Hill Country, and I get my water from wells. My drainage is *via* septic tanks that "catch" *whatever* comes **from** my kitchen sink, from my bath and shower, and *whatever* is **flushed down** the toilets.

Also, what guarantee do I have that if my animals *urinate* in January, that I am not *bathing* in it, or *drinking* "it" in April? The septic tanks are sunk into the ground with a *drain field* connected.

When the tank gets full, that "whatever" that is in it (the shower water, kitchen sink water and TOILET *contents*) overflows and empties into that "drain field," comprised of a series of pipes with holes in them; and THIS seeps into the ground.

My father-in-law, an engineer, told me *"Not to worry. This surface leakage only goes down a few feet and never reaches the water table."*

Well, *my* reasoning is that it is ON the ground, and if rain water finds its way down to the water table, how come that "whatever" doesn't? Beside, just the *thought* concerns me!

Ugh! When you think about it for a moment, it certainly *sounds* horrible. *AS A GUARANTEE,* you can bet that I have a water purifier in my home and office, even in my *barns* in the event I decide to grab a fast drink from a garden hose on these hot Texas days.

I cannot WAIT for the Federal Government to gather 650 BILLION to solve this problem. It may NEVER happen. That is why **I—YOU—WE** must do something about it ourselves.

THERE IS A DANGER

My part is not to try and FRIGHTEN you, but to INFORM you. I'm not trying to SELL you anything. As a research journalist, I FIND the problem areas and I also look for ANSWERS. I **"RESEARCH THE RESEARCHERS"** and put *THEIR* findings in this book in words most can understand

One discomforting fact I recall reading about happened several years ago to some kids in Minnesota who found FROGS that looked like *mutants*. Some (the frogs) had four hind legs, eyes growing on their KNEES, mouths that were horribly misshapen, and several other obvious abnormalities. Scientists determined it was due to the unidentified *toxic chemicals* in the pond and ground water.

MORE WORRIES: ONE in SIX people *drink* water that is **contaminated** by excessive amounts of *lead*. In the early summer, HALF the rivers and streams in America's *corn belt* (Iowa, Nebraska, Indiana, South Dakota, Minnesota, Ohio, Wisconsin, most of Illinois and parts of Kansas) were laced with dangerous levels of pesticides.

We recently had some heavy rains here in Texas. The water ran though the Hill Country where there are farms and ranches and many small homesteads that have septic tanks. This "stuff" FROM these septic tanks was carried to the rivers and INTO the water system.

Do you know that microbes in tap water are responsible for at least *one in three* gastrointestinal illnesses? According to the *Natural Resources Defense Council* nearly a million people a year are affected by drinking CONTAMINATED water. And in a closer to home concern, San Antonio, that has a terrific water supply system, just voted to have FLUORIDE put into their water!

The Federal Government is finally being forced to admit that outdated water treatment facilities *throughout the country* are incapable of coping with the flood of environmental TOXINS that are permeating the nation's water supply.

The widespread use of CHLORINE as the primary means of disinfecting water *is ineffective* against the increasing number of dangerous pathogens that are in the nation's water supply. In yet *another* study, new research says that the ingestion of CHLORINATED water may be a primary cause of cancer and heart diseases.

And FLUORIDATION (to prevent tooth decay) is being put into these water systems. Who made these guys dentists? Many knowledgeable critics say that fluoridation presents an unacceptable *risk* to health because of its effect on the body's *immune system*, as well as its potential genetic and carcinogenic effects.

Here is a LIST of the agencies that **DO NOT** endorse *fluoridation* in water. These are but a few, but there are more. I could have filled several pages with agencies and studies all around the world. I'm hoping that these are sufficient **NON**-endorsements for some of these cities that have plans to fluoridate their water.

✦ The American HEART Association.
✦ The American DIABETES Association
✦ American Academy of Allergy & Immunology
✦ The American CANCER Society.
✦ American Civil Liberties Union
✦ The National KIDNEY Foundation
✦ The American PSYCHIATRIC Association

Few things are as insidious as BAD WATER. It's dangerous for you and your children, but you usually can't tell by *drinking* it. And if you *do* have "problems" with it , you may NOT be able to find out *where* the problems are coming from.

Water can carry some of our most serious diseases; **typhoid, dysentery, hepatitis,** and STILL look clear in the glass. It MUST be tested and it MUST be purified.

There are 10,700+bladder and rectal cancers per year (about 30 cancers per DAY) from drinking a single glass of *contaminated* water that LOOKS clear; TWICE the number than die from fires and more than are killed each year by handguns.

This is not a NEW problem. I have watched headlines for years that talk about the dangers of **chlorine, lead, fluoride** and **parasites** in our drinking water. Yes, you **need** to find out what's in YOUR water and then do something about it.

NEWSFLASH

On June 27, 2002 it was announced on CNN that ALL INFORMATION regarding tap water will be REMOVED from public access (EPA web site) and turned over to Homeland Security. Their reasoning? Bio-terrorism.

I am a loyal American. I do not suspect that every person in government is a liar, cheat, thief, drunk, or a womanizer. I know many of these people; and they are *good* people; many dedicate their lives to helping our nation.

I also feel that this is a *"crock"* in that these terrorists KNOW where our power plants and water supply systems are. If they don't already know, they can listen to the news, and one newscast or another will TELL them where we are vulnerable.

It comes down to the fact that it is a *"money thing."* It would cost the Federal Government upwards of **650 BILLION DOLLARS** to correct the problem with our water supply systems in this country, to rid it of these detrimental chemicals that do so much harm. But WHEN will they do it?

I am telling that it is up to US—to you and me—to take care of this problem ourselves and our loved ones and make water safe in our own home. We can do it! I'll tell you what I've done (and found out) and then it's your choice.

ALL of these people, and all of these re-searchers, and all of these study groups *can't* be wrong when they tell us that our water is unsafe. I could fill a book with testimonials from research groups so thick you'd need a dolly to carry it.

The newspapers and magazines that carried these stories are not the *Globe, SUN,* or **The National Enquirer**, but ones that are *credible* and have a stringent format, and if the facts are incorrect or the truth is stretched just for *shock value,* they won't print the story.

Our entire water supply is contaminated according to the *Environmental Protection Agency.* Think about it. Residue from pesticides, herbicides, fertilizers, and industrial waste ALL come into contact with our drinking water. And, do ANIMALS count?

What about the hundreds of thousands of *gasoline storage tanks* in the United States; MANY LEAK! And where do you think this gasoline goes? And so called *"land fills"* and *"toxic waste dumps"* are in every city, small or large. We were careless in the past and we must do something NOW!

According to the *National Academy of Sciences*, arsenic can cause cancer, heart disease, and perhaps diabetes. *Arsenic-tainted water* is most common in the West and Southwest. Some arsenic occurs naturally in soil, while some comes from industrial waste.

Another problem with our drinking water is with PARASITES! *Cryptospordium* (pronounced crip-toe-spo-RID-ee-um) is a parasite that lives in the intestines of humans and animals.

In 1993, in Milwaukee, for but one single *week,* there was a breakdown in their water sanitation system and ONE HUNDRED people DIED. Almost half a MILLION **more** suffered from diarrhea, stomach cramps and fever.

WHAT IS THE SOLUTION?

I search for answers to these problems and I find them. I want this book to help you **understand** these dangers. I, personally, do not *like* drinking a lot of water. But, now with my *Spring House* and *Living Water* system in my home (offices and barns) I feel safe, and it DOES taste better.

The very *best answer* is a WATER PURIFICATION UNIT. On the following page I have a CHART that tells WHY I prefer this *Spring House* and *Living Water*. Remember, *"I don't sell 'em, I just use 'em!"*

How Spring House Compares
to other whole-home water treatment systems

	Reverse Osmosis	Carbon Filtration	Distiller	Stand-Alone Ultraviolet	Water Softener	SPRING HOUSE
Reduces Microorganisms	✔	☹	★	✔	☹	★
Reduces Parasitic Cysts	★	❖	★	☹	☹	★
Reduces Dissolved Lead	★	❖	★	☹	☹	★
Reduces Chlorine	★	★	★	☹	☹	★
Energy Efficient	✔	★	☹	✔	✔	★
User Maintainable	✔	❖	☹	★	❖	★
Proper Function Easily Verified	✔	✔	✔	✔	✔	★
Water Efficient (No Waste Stream)	☹	★	☹	★	★	★
Convenient	✔	✔	✔	★	☹	★

★ Excellent　　✔ Good　　❖ Varies　　☹ Poor

Even though we can travel coast to coast in America and drink water that is *supposedly* safe, **is it safe?** There's no GUARANTEE that this water *won't* make you sick! *Much* of it contains chlorine.

Chlorine as a disinfectant did wonders, BUT it can combine with decaying leaves and other naturally-occurring organic matter to form compounds called "*disinfection byproducts.*" Let's look at how other units compare with mine.

Kenneth Cantor, epidemiologist at the *National Cancer Institute* in Bethesda, Maryland says, "*The disinfection byproducts in our water can roughly DOUBLE the risk of developing bladder cancer.*" There are other illnesses believed to be caused by unsafe drinking water.

If your water appears cloudy, the term "*turbidity*" means that particles of clay, silt, decaying plants, parasites and other matter have become suspended in the water.

Then there is LEAD, and about 40 million Americans drink water that contains *excess* lead. According to the EPA, lead builds up in the body over many years and can damage the brain, kidneys, and red blood cells.

Water picks up this lead anywhere from the plant to the tap—in holding tanks, underground pipes, lead pipes, and fixtures. The NEW systems use plastic which is *more* safe, but there are still *some* systems with lead pipes and solder, and ones that are illegally installed to save money.

BOTTLED WATER

Is bottled water safer than tap water? That depends on WHERE the bottled water comes from, IF its been treated, and HOW. Much of it comes from natural springs, or from municipal aquifers, and *"measurable"* amounts of contaminants—such as lead—are allowed.

In an analysis by the *Natural Resource and Defense Council*, only about a DOZEN of the 103 brands of bottled water tested between 1993 and 1999 exceeded federal, state or industry guidelines. Short of testing for YOURSELF there IS NO WAY to guarantee that even bottled water is *free of contaminates*.

PURIFIED water is that which has been treated with distillation, ion-exchange, reverse osmosis or a similar process. This process gets rid of *most* contaminants, but not *benzene, chlorine* and other volatile organic chemicals.

AUTHOR'S CLOSING COMMENTS

That's it! I could go on and on and write a book the size of *War and Peace* about indoor polluted air and unsafe water. This book is to make you aware that there are problems and yes, YOU are the only answer. Now, you know what I know. It's up to you to do something about it. Act now!

To those of you reading this book who *sell* air or water purification units, I commend you. Call, fax, write or email me and I'll send you a **FREE** *Information Packet* on how I am willing to help you.

You are helping others, and I want to help YOU accomplish that goal.

Good luck and God bless,
Pete Billac

THESE ARE EXCELLENT BOOKS ON WATER

DON'T DRINK THE WATER by Lono Kahuna Kupua A'O, $11.95 email: kalipres@rmi.net or order line 1-888-999-5254

WATER (The Shocking Truth) by Paul and Patricia Bragg, $7.95 email: brag@brag.com or tel 1-805-968-1020

ABOUT THE AUTHOR

PETE BILLAC has written 53 full-length books, 46 of which have become best sellers. He is one of the most sought-after speakers in America. He makes his audiences laugh— hard—while he delivers his *messages* with candor, quick wit and an ever-present winning smile. His books are sold worldwide and are published in over 30 languages.

Pete is a true maverick; he writes what he chooses to write. His topics range from adventure to war, the Mafia, health, famous people, romance and motivation. He turns down book offers daily. ONLY if he believes in something does he write about it.

He conducts seminars for Fortune 500 companies on marketing, he lectures at universities and he is also booked for talks on cruise ships. He is FUNNY! He charms all audiences. He mixes common sense with laughter and he breathes *life* into every topic.

Perhaps you've seen Pete on Donahue, Sally Jessy Raphael, Good Morning America, Laff Stop or other national televison shows. He is on the radio daily both in the US and in countries across the world. His energy and enthusiasm is boundless.

Presently he is giving presentations on THE SILENT KILLERS to overflow audiences in the United States and Canada. He is a *must-see* and *must-hear* personality.

"Pete is an expert at restoring self-confidence and self-esteem in others . . ."

Phil Donahue, *National Television Talk Show Host*

THE SILENT KILLERS

is available in quantity discounts through:

Swan Publishing

1059 CR 100
Burnet, TX 78611

Phone: (512) 756-6800
Fax: (512) 756-0102
e-mail: swanbooks@ghg.net

Visit our web site at:
http:\\www.swan-pub.com

For additional information

*After reading this book, please pass it on to
a friend or relative. It could change their
lives for the better—FOREVER.*